Eight Cinderellas

By Nancy Polette

Cover by Greg Lawhun and John Steele
1997 Published by Pieces of Learning

www.piecesoflearning.com

CLC0207
ISBN 1-880505-57-6
Printed in the U.S.A.

CONTENTS

Eight Cinderellas by Nancy Polette

Introduction

Every country has its Cinderella tale, in fact, there are 347 known versions of this popular story. Learning about the culture and customs of nations throughout the world can be exciting when using a Cinderella tale from each country as a starting point.
For example: Look at the elements of culture revealed in this Appalachian tale:

> *Ashpet, an Appalachian Tale* retold by Joan Compton. Illustrated by Kenn Compton. Holiday House, 1994.
> Long ago, in a cabin by Eagle's Nest Mountain, lived a servant girl called Ashpet. All day long, she chopped firewood, washed clothes, and cooked and cleaned for the widow Hooper and her cranky daughters. Ashpet had so much work to do, the widow wouldn't even allow her to go to the annual church picnic.
> Ashpet's life changes for the better, however, when old Granny shows up and works some magic. How Ashpet outshines the widow's daughters and captures the heart of the doctor's son (all in her red calico dress and red shoes) makes for a delightful tale where washtubs can't defeat true love!

As each tale is presented (each from a different country) student-ready activities are included to bring joy to the reading experience. For example: Let's sing a song about Ashpet! Follow the pattern to write another verse.

Ashpet (Sing to "Are You Sleeping?")

Overworked   Ashpet
adjective   name
Pretty   Ashpet
adjective   name
(Where?) In the cabin
(Where?) On the road
(Doing what?) Scrubbing and washing
(Doing what?) Chopping and cooking
Poor Ashpet. Poor Ashpet.

As with many activities in this book the song helps children to sequence the story and at the same time enjoy creating verses and singing about *Ashpet. The activities for The Egyptian Cinderella, The Korean Cinderella, Mufaro's Beautiful Daughters, Princess Furball, The Rough Face Girl, Tattercoats, Vasilisa the Beautiful* and *Yeh Shen* are varied and teach skills as well as knowledge about the country of origin in divergent and exciting ways.

The Egyptian Cinderella by Shirley Climo. HarperCollins, 1989.

Booktalk

In the Land of Egypt where the green Nile River widens to meet the blue sea, lives a maiden called Rhodopes (ra-doh-pes). Because she is Greek and a slave, Rhodopes is scorned by the Egyptian house servants. She has only her rose-red gold slippers which flash like fireflies when she dances. When a falcon swoops down and snatches a slipper away, Rhodopes is heartbroken. How is she to know that the falcon has delivered the slipper to the great Pharaoh himself? She cannot guess that the Pharaoh will search all of Egypt to find the owner of the tiny shoe and make her his queen. Will he be successful? To find out, read *The Egyptian Cinderella.*

The Booktalk as a Readers Theatre Script

Reading Parts: Narrator One, Narrator Two, Rhodopes, Pharaoh, Falcon

Narrator One: In the Land of Egypt where the green Nile River widens to meet the blue sea, lives a maiden called Rhodopes (ra-doh-pes). Because she is

Rhodopes: Greek and a slave,

Narrator One: Rhodopes is scorned by the Egyptian house servants. She has only her

Rhodopes: rose-red gold slippers which flash like fireflies

Narrator One: when she dances.

Narrator Two: When a falcon

Falcon: swoops down and snatches a slipper away,

Narrator One: Rhodopes is heartbroken.

Narrator Two: How is she to know that the falcon

Falcon: has delivered the slipper to the great Pharaoh himself?

Narrator Two: She cannot guess that the Pharaoh

Pharaoh: will search all of Egypt to find the owner of the tiny shoe

ALL: and make her his queen. Will he be successful? To find out, read *The Egyptian Cinderella.*

2. In this tale as Rhodopes washed the clothes, ground the grain and weeded the garden, many animals became her friends. Birds ate crumbs from her hand, a monkey sat on her shoulder and she sang to a hippopotamus. If you had jobs to do outside, what animals or birds might keep you company? Name as many as you can.

3. Chanting the story.

You will need three groups for this chant. All groups chant at the same time. If you keep the rhythm, all three groups should get to the line, "Pharaoh's near, has a shoe" at the same time.

Group One
Beat the gong, beat the gong, beat the gong, the barge comes.
Beat the gong, beat the gong, beat the gong, the barge comes.
Pharaoh's near, has a shoe
Who's the owner, is it you?

Group Two
Sails of silk, flying high, sails of silk, touch the sky.
Sails of silk, flying high, sails of silk, touch the sky.
Pharaoh's near, has a shoe
Who's the owner, is it you?

Group Three
Rhodopes is frightened and flees in alarm, the Pharaoh is here but means no harm,
Holds up the slipper, says "I'll give life
To the one it fits, she'll be my wife."
Pharaoh's near, has a shoe
Who's the owner, is it you?

4. Draw a story map showing Alexandria (Rhodopes' city by the sea) and the path of the Nile River that leads to Memphis. Use as many details from the story as you can. On your map, one inch will equal 25 miles.
   A. If it takes two days to pole up river 50 miles and the journey lasted 6 days, how far was it from Alexandria to Memphis?
   B. On your map, how many inches long will the route be?
   C. As you illustrate your map, what plants and animals from the story can you add?
   D. What kinds of river transportation will you show?

Answers to 4A and B: A. 150 miles B. six inches

5. How we read makes a difference!
   Read this one line from the story accenting the word in caps. Tell what you think the line means when read this way.
   A. NOW we will see the Pharaoh.
      Meaning: ______________________________
   B. Now WE will see the Pharaoh.
      Meaning: ______________________________
   C. Now we will SEE the Pharaoh.
      Meaning: ______________________________
   D. Now we will see the PHARAOH.
      Meaning: ______________________________

6. Play the "I Have, Who Has" Game. Cut apart the strips and give one to each of six players. The player who has the strip with two stars ** reads the "Who Has" part of his/her strip. The player who can answer correctly reads the "I Have" part of his/her strip and then reads the "Who Has" portion. The game continues until all strips are read.

I HAVE:	The Pharaoh saw Rhodopes peering from the rushes.
**WHO HAS:	Who was brought to Egypt and sold as a slave?

I HAVE:	Rhodopes was brought to Egypt and sold as a slave.
WHO HAS:	How was Rhodopes treated by the other servants?

I HAVE:	Rhodopes was scorned by the servants and made to do all the work.
WHO HAS:	What happened to Rhodopes' beautiful slipper?

I HAVE:	The slipper was stolen by a falcon and taken to the Pharaoh.
WHO HAS:	What did the Pharaoh do with the slipper?

I HAVE:	The Pharaoh carried the slipper with him to find the owner and make her his wife.
WHO HAS:	What did Rhodopes do when the Pharaoh's barge appeared?

I HAVE:	Rhodopes hid in the rushes when the Pharaoh appeared.
WHO HAS:	How did the Pharaoh find Rhodopes?

Pick A Project!
A Research Organizer

Step One: Choose and circle one action word	**Step Two: Choose and circle one topic**	**Step Three: Choose and circle one product**
	Literature-Related Topics	
Label	The Land of Egypt as the setting for the story.	Acrostic poem
List	The use of similes in describing Rhodopes	Chart
Describe	The contrasting natures of Rhodopes and of the servant girls	Story
Locate	A song Rhodopes might have sung to the hippopotamus.	Model
Report	The Pharaoh in this story and the Prince in Cinderella.	Map
Show	The role of the falcon in the story.	Mobile
Group	Non Fiction Topics	Diorama
Discover	The Nile River	Bio-poem
Compose	Animals of Egypt	Report
Create	Many uses of papyrus	True/false book
Demonstrate	The great pyramids	Drawing
Choose	River travel in ancient Egypt	List report
Tell About	Products and crops of Egypt	Song
		Interview

Write a sentence telling what you will do to report on the topic you choose. In your sentence include an action word and a product as well as your topic.

action product topic

I will **compose** a **song** about the **products and crops** of Egypt.

Activity: Compose a song about Egypt.

Research: Find

1. The capital of present day Egypt ______________________
2. A large city in present day Egypt _____________________
3. Three products (mined or manufactured) ________________,
   ______________________ and __________________________
4. Three crops _________________________, _________________
   and ______________________________

   Use this information in the song below. Sing to "She'll Be Coming Round the Mountain."

   She'll be coming from __________________________________
   (Capital)
   When she comes.
   She'll be coming from __________________________________
   (Large City)
   When she comes,
   She'll bring (three products __________________, ___________________,
   ____
   She'll bring (three crops) ___________________, ____________________,
   and _________________________.
   She'll be coming from EGYPT when she comes.

5. Look on a map and find another country that is a close neighbor of Egypt. Find the capital, a large city, three products and three crops and use the song pattern above to write a song about that country.

6. Use the same pattern and write a song about the State or Province in which you live.

The Korean Cinderella by Shirley Climo. Illustrated by Ruth Heller. HarperCollins, 1993.

Booktalk

In the land of Korea, where magical creatures are as common as cabbages, lives a child named Pear Blossom. Pear Blossom is as lovely as the pear tree planted in celebration of her birth, but she is mistreated by Omoni, her jealous stepmother. Omoni forces her to rise before the sun and cook and clean until midnight, and demands that Pear Blossom complete three tasks no human could possibly do alone. She is to fill a water jar with a hole in it the size of an onion; hull and polish every grain of rice from a huge sack scattered all over the courtyard and; weed the rice paddies in less than a day, paddies that spread out before her like a great green lake. But Pear Blossom is not alone. Three magical animals assist her, a gigantic frog, a flock of sparrows and a huge black ox. It is with the help of these creatures that Pear Blossom is able to attend the festival and becomes a nobleman's wife.

The Booktalk as a Readers Theatre Script

Reading Parts: Pear Blossom, Narrator One, Omoni, Narrator Two, Frog, Sparrow, Ox

Narrator One: In the land of Korea,

Frog/Sparrow/Ox: where magical creatures are as common as cabbages,

Narrator One: lives a child named Pear Blossom. Pear Blossom is

Pearl Blossom: as lovely as the pear tree

Narrator One: planted in celebration of her birth,

Narrator Two: but she is mistreated by Omoni,

Omoni: her jealous stepmother.

Narrator Two: Omoni forces her

Omoni: to rise before the sun

Pearl Blossom: and cook and clean until midnight, and demands that

Omoni: Pear Blossom complete three tasks no human could possibly do alone. She is to

Pearl Blossom: fill a water jar with a hole in it the size of an onion;

Omoni: hull and polish every grain of rice from a huge sack scattered all over the courtyard and;

Pearl Blossom: weed the rice paddies in less than a day,

Narrator One: paddies that spread out before her like a great green lake. But Pear Blossom

Animals: is not alone.

Narrator Two:	Three magical animals
Animals:	assist her,
Frog:	a gigantic frog,
Sparrow:	a flock of sparrows
Ox:	and a huge black ox.
Narrator Two:	It is with the help of these creatures
Narrator One:	that Pear Blossom
Pear Blossom:	is able to attend the festival
ALL:	and becomes a nobleman's wife.

Analyzing Story Structure

Story Structure

Explain how the parts are related to the whole. What would happen if one part were missing?Remember: A well written story must have characters, setting and a plot.

A good story is a problem-solving exercise. The author must set up a problem and solve it.

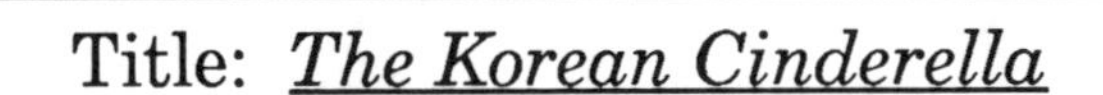

Setting: cottage/courtyard, rice paddies, road/festival

Characters: Pear Blossom, Omoni, frog, sparrows, ox, nobleman

The Problem: cruelty of the stepmother

Goal: Pear Blossom to be free of her stepmother, attend the festival

Episodes:
1. Pear Blossom to fill the jar while others go to festival
2. She must polish the grain
3. She must weed the rice paddies
4. Magical animals help so that she sets off for the festival.
5. Sees a nobleman on the road, loses her sandal.
6. Nobleman finds the sandal and seeks and finds its owner.

Resolution:
Pear Blossom and the Nobleman are wed.

A Sight and Sound Poem

The sights and sounds of Korea, Pear Blossom's land, are very different from those of your country. Choose one of the story settings below. Follow the pattern and write a sight and sound poem about it.

Cottage courtyard the pebbled road
the stream the festival

Reread the story and list sight and sound words you find about the place you choose. You may add other sight and sound words.

Example:

Place:	The rice fields
Sight (1)	Spread out like a great, green lake
Sight (2)	Rows and rows of rippling rice plants
Sight (3)	Ugly weeds rising above the grain
Sound (two lines)	Whish, whoo, whish, whoo,
	Whish, swish, swish, swish.

Place:	The rice fields
Sight (4)	Twisted through with a whirlwind
Sight (5)	The giant black ox munching weeds
Sight (6)	Roaring up from a cloud of dust.
Sound (two lines)	Do-o-o, munch, clomp, clomp, thud.
	Do-o-o, munch, clomp, clomp, thud!

Your Turn

Place: ________________________________
Sight (1) ________________________________
Sight (2) ________________________________
Sight (3) ________________________________
Sound (two lines) ________________________________
____

Place: ________________________________
Sight (4) ________________________________
Sight (5) ________________________________
Sight (6) ________________________________
Sound (two lines) ________________________________
____

	Pick A Project! A Research Organizer	
Step One: Choose and circle one action word	**Step Two: Choose and circle one topic**	**Step Three: Choose and circle one product**
Label List Describe Locate Report Show Group Discover Compose Create Demonstrate Choose Tell About	<u>Literature-Related Topics</u> How Pear Blossom is mistreated by her stepmother. The role of the magical creatures in the story. How Omoni is alike or different from the stepmother in Hansel and Gretel. How Pear Blossom is like other Cinderellas. <u>Non Fiction Topics</u> A typical Korean meal How rice is grown Why the Ox is important in farming in Korea How North Korea and South Korea are alike What you would see at a Korean country festival	Acrostic poem Chart Story Model Map Mobile Diorama Bio-poem Report True/false book Drawing List report Song Interview

Write a sentence telling what you will do to report on the topic you choose. In your sentence include an action word and a product as well as your topic.

action topic product

I will **describe how rice is grown** in a **process report**.

About Korea

Korea is a peninsula that juts out into the Sea of Japan. Since the Korean War of 1953, the peninsula is now two countries, North Korea and South Korea. Many Koreans still live as their ancestors lived hundreds of years ago. They live in small houses with thatched roofs and farm the ground with crude tools. Four out of five Koreans are farmers. They grow rice as their main crop.

A Report on Growing Rice

I wonder why...They
irrigate the land
scatter the seeds
plow the ground
weed the fields
flood the paddies
cut the stalks
tie in sheaves
dry the crop
separate the grains
remove the hulls
polish the kernels
send to market
When they could grow potatoes
INSTEAD.

Use this same pattern for a report on one of the favorite foods in the United States and Canada...the potato

I WONDER WHY THEY....
____
____
____
____
____
____
When they could grow
____

INSTEAD.

Mufaro's Beautiful Daughters written and illustrated by John Steptoe. Scholastic, 1987.

1. **A pre-reading activity.**
On the cover of the book are pictures of Mufaro's daughters. Manyara is on the front cover and Nyasha on the back. From looking at the pictures ask students to predict which of these words would best describe Manyara and which would best describe Nyasha. Put an N for words that describe Nyasha and a M for words that describe Manyara. If a word fits neither girl, leave the line blank. Support or deny guesses by hearing or reading the booktalk.

_____ arrogant	_____ awkward	_____ anxious
_____ admired	_____ agreeable	_____ bold
_____ bullying	_____ beautiful	_____ concerned
_____ cruel	_____ cranky	_____ cheerful
_____ courteous	_____ comforting	_____ disagreeable
_____ foolish	_____ faithful	_____ frightened
_____ gentle	_____ impatient	_____ jealous
_____ kind	_____ mean	_____ unselfish

Booktalk

Mufaro and his two beautiful daughters lived in a small African village. Nyasha was caring and courteous and agreeable to all while Manyara was disagreeable, selfish and demanding. When a messenger from the city announced that the king wished to choose a wife and had invited "the most worthy and beautiful daughters in the land", to appear before him, Manyara left the village long before the others hoping to be the first to see the king.

On her journey Manyara refused to give food to a small boy, scolded an old woman for giving advice and was rude to a man with his head tucked under his arm.

The next morning when Mufaro and Nyasha set out for the city, Nyasha took a moment to say goodbye to her friend Nyoka, a garden snake. Along the way she shared food with a small boy, gave a gift to an old woman in thanks for her advice and was polite to the man with a head tucked under his arm.

As Mufaro and Nyasha neared the palace, Manyara met them with anxious cries. Something terrible was waiting in the king's chamber! Although Nyasha was frightened by her sister's words, she anxiously opened the door and entered the chamber. Then she smiled at what she saw. Can you guess the happy ending to this tale? Find out if you are right by reading *Mufaro's Beautiful Daughters*.

The Booktalk as a Readers Theatre Script

Reading Parts:	Narrator One, Narrator Two, Mufaro, Nyasha, Manyara, Messenger
Narrator One:	Mufaro and his two beautiful daughters
Mufaro/Daughters:	lived in a small African village.
Narrator One:	Nyasha was
Nyasha:	caring and courteous and agreeable to all
Narrator Two:	while Manyara was
Manyara:	disagreeable, selfish and demanding.
Narrator Two:	When a messenger from the city announced that
Messenger:	the king wished to choose a wife and had invited "the most worthy and beautiful daughters in the land to appear before him,
Narrator Two:	Manyara
Manyara:	left the village long before the others hoping to be the first to see the king.
Narrator Two:	On her journey Manyara refused
Manyara:	to give food to a small boy, scolded an old woman for giving advice and was rude to a man with his head tucked under his arm.
Narrator One:	The next morning when Mufaro and Nyasha set out for the city, Nyasha
Nyasha:	took a moment to say goodbye
Narrator One:	to her friend Nyoka, a garden snake. Along the way she
Nyasha:	shared food with a small boy, gave a gift to an old woman in thanks for her advice and was polite to the man with a head tucked under his arm.
Narrator One:	As Mufaro and Nyasha
Mufaro/Nyasha:	neared the palace,
Narrator Two:	Manyara
Manyara:	met them with anxious cries. Something terrible was waiting in the king's chamber!
Narrator One:	Although Nyasha was frightened by her sister's words, she anxiously
Myasha:	opened the door and entered the chamber.
Both Narrators:	Then she smiled at what she saw. Can you guess the happy ending to this tale?
ALL:	Find out if you are right by reading *Mufaro's Beautiful Daughters*.

2. Manyara suffered because she refused to take the old woman's advice. Work with a partner or small group to advise Manyara as to how she might lead a happier life. Think of many ways to present the advice. Choose the way your group likes best and share your advice with the class.

Advice Ideas:

A. Try free verse. Begin this way:

   Listen once, listen twice,
   For you, Manyara, we have advice.
   You must:
   1. ______________________________
   2. ______________________________
   3. ______________________________
   4. ______________________________
   And here is more! Try
   5. ______________________________
   6. ______________________________
   7. ______________________________
   8. ______________________________
   It's too late now to be the king's wife.
   But follow this advice and you'll lead a happy life.

B. Look in the newspaper for headlines and words from advertisements. Cut out words you think would be good "advice" words for Manyara.

C. Make a collage of pictures from old magazines that show the kinds of things Manyara should do to lead a happier life.

D. Search the poetry shelf in the library for poems that give good advice. Copy and illustrate one of the poems for Manyara.

E. Go to the art shelf in the library for books of famous paintings. Find three paintings that show people doing the kinds of things Manyara should do (instead of being selfish). Write a sentence or two telling why you chose each painting.

F. Illustrate one or more of the words from #1 on page twelve that Manyara should pay more attention to.

	Pick A Project! A Research Organizer	
Step One: **Choose and circle one action word**	**Step Two:** **Choose and circle one topic**	**Step Three:** **Choose and circle one product**
Label List Describe Locate Report Show Group Discover Compose Create Demonstrate Choose Tell About	<u>Literature-Related Topics</u> Nyasha and Manyara The African village as the setting for the story The significance of the boy, the woman and the man with his head under his arm Mufaro's Beautiful Daughters and the French Cinderella The role of the garden snake in the story <u>Non Fiction Topics</u> An African market place A small African village Birds of Africa Snakes of Africa The likenesses and differences of two African countries...for example, Nigeria and Egypt or South Africa and Ghana Animals found in the grasslands, mountains, jungles, deserts and coastal areas of Africa	Acrostic poem Chart Story Model Map Mobile Diorama Bio-poem Report True/false book Drawing List report Song Interview

Write a sentence telling what you will do to report on the topic you choose. In your sentence include an action word and a product as well as your topic.

action topic product
I will **describe an African market place** using a **five senses poem**.

The Market Place

There are many similarities between the Mall that you and your family visit and the African market place. Both are filled with hundreds of different sights and sounds and smells. In the Mall you might smell cookies baking. In the African market place smells would be of cooking meat and of fresh fruits and vegetables like coconuts, dates, cassava, tomatoes and yams. Instead of finding clothing on racks as you do in the Mall, you would see clothing spread out on straw mats along with baskets and wood carvings and jewelry. At special times of the year in many Malls, there are singing or instrumental groups. At the African market place there are strolling musicians with drums and flutes and kundis. And just as you and your family do, the African market place is often a place where friends meet and chat about the latest family doings.

Use the five senses model below to describe both the African market place and the Mall you visit.

The African market place is the color of ________________

It sounds like ____

It tastes like ____

It smells like ____

It looks like ____

It makes me feel like ________________________________

The ____________ Mall is the color of ________________

It sounds like ____

It tastes like ____

It smells like ____

It looks like ____

It makes me feel like ________________________________

Princess Furball by Charlotte Huck. Illustrated by Anita Lobel. Greenwillow Books, 1989.

Booktalk

Once upon a time a cruel king betrothed his motherless daughter to an Ogre in exchange for fifty wagons of silver. To prevent the marriage, the princess told her father she must have three bridal gifts — a dress as golden as the sun, another as silver as the moon and a third as glittering as the stars. In addition she asked for a coat made of a thousand different kinds of fur. Thinking her requests were impossible to meet, imagine her surprise when her father presented her with every gift. The only path open to her is to run away, and run she does until found by hunters and taken to a far away castle where she worked as a maid to the servants...fetching wood, drawing water, sweeping ashes and "doing all the rest of the dirty work no one else wanted to do." Scullery maids never meet kings..or do they? Read *Princess Furball* to discover how her life changes.

The Booktalk as a Readers Theatre Script

Reading Parts: Narrator One, Narrator Two, Princess, Cruel King

Narrator Two: Once upon a time a cruel king betrothed his motherless daughter

King: to an Ogre in exchange for fifty wagons of silver.

Narrator One: To prevent the marriage, the princess told her father she must have

Princess: three bridal gifts — a dress as golden as the sun, another as silver as the moon and a third as glittering as the stars.

Narrator One: In addition she asked for

Princess: a coat made of a thousand different kinds of fur.

Narrator Two: Thinking her requests were impossible to meet, imagine her surprise when her father

King: presented her with every gift.

Narrator One: The only path open to her

Princess: is to run away,

Narrator One: and run she does until found by hunters and taken to a far away castle where she worked as a maid to the servants...

Princess: fetching wood, drawing water, sweeping ashes and "doing all the rest of the dirty work no one else wanted to do."

Narrator One: Scullery maids never meet kings..

ALL: or do they? Read *Princess Furball* to discover how her life changes.

Princess Furball continued.

Creative Thinking

Develop warm-up activities for *Princess Furball* by Charlotte Huck

Fluency: The ability to make many responses.
Name all the possible jobs that might need to be done in a castle.

Flexibility: Finding new categories. Stretching the mind beyond the expected response.
How can you group the items you named under fluency?
Group the jobs you named. For example, some jobs might be related to defending the castle, others to feeding the people.

Originality: Responding in new or original ways.
What group and/or items did you name that no one else named?

Elaboration: Adding details to make a product more complete.
What could you add to canned tomato soup to make it more delicious so that everyone would ask for more?

Planning: Determining a task to be done, the steps to take, materials needed and possible problems.
Pretend you are the castle cook and the King is giving a feast. What would you have to do first, second? What problems might you encounter?

Forecasting: Determining cause and effect.
What might cause a King to sell his daughter to an Ogre?
What might cause a young princess to run away?

Decision Making and Problem Solving
A. Examine the facts
B. State the problem
C. List alternatives
D. List criteria for judging alternatives
E. Score alternatives on a decision grid
F. State solution

A cruel King promised his daughter in marriage to an Ogre in exchange for fifty wagons of silver. The Princess does not want to marry the Ogre. Use the grid below to help her decide the best course of action. Note: The Princess has no money of her own.

	Criteria					Totals
Score: 1=no, 2=maybe, 3=yes **Alternatives**	Is it fast?	Is it safe?	Can she do it alone?	Low cost?	Will it work?	
Pretend she is very ill.	3	2	3	3	1	12

Evaluation: Judging the pros and cons of an item or situation.If the king needs money to run his Kingdom it is okay to marry his daughter to the Ogre for fifty wagons of silver? List reasons for both yes and no.

Princess Furball continued.

Skills From Story Illustrations

Teacher Note: any illustration can be used.
Responding to illustrations: Sentence Sense

PRINCESS FURBALL

Based on the picture, write:

An interrogative sentence:

____

____

____

____

An imperative sentence:

____

____

____

____

An exclamatory sentence:

____

____

____

____

A sentence which contains a proper noun, a possessive noun, a plural noun and a contraction.

____

____

A sentence with a homonym.

____

____

A sentence that contains two nouns, three adjectives, two words with prefixes and suffixes, one or more verbs and at least one prepositional phrase.

____

____

Princess Furball continued.

Pick A Project!
A Research Organizer

Step One: Choose and circle one action word	**Step Two: Choose and circle one topic**	**Step Three: Choose and circle one product**
Label List Describe Locate Report Show Group Discover Compose Create Demonstrate Choose Tell About	<u>Literature-Related Topics</u> Ways in which the old nurse prepared Princess Furball for her future role as a queen. Reasons the father would sell his daughter to an ogre. Coincidence in the story (example: Young King out hunting just as Furball was napping in the tree) Why Furball waited through three balls to reveal herself to the King <u>Non Fiction Topics</u> Fur-bearing animals of the forest Life in a castle in the Middle Ages Recipe for soup which contains items from every food group Many jobs to be done in a castle One day in the life of a King.	Acrostic poem Chart Story Model Mobile Diorama Bio-poem Report Process Report Drawing List report Song Interview

Write a sentence telling what you will do to report on the topic you choose. In your sentence include an action word and a product as well as your topic.

action topic product
I will **tell about one day in the life of a king** in a **process report.**

The Process Report

Use the Process Report to tell how something is done. Note the "twist" at the end.
Here is a Process Report describing one day in the life of Princess Furball after she is taken to the castle by the hunters.

I WONDER WHY.....I
Open my eyes
In the dark woodshed,
Wash my face
Put on my clothes
Cover myself with the fur coat
Fetch the wood
Draw the water
Stir the fire
Pluck the chickens
Clean the vegetables
Wash the dishes
Sweep the ashes
And do dirty work no one else wants to do
When I could
Marry the rich ogre instead.

Write a Process Report about one day in the life of a King. A good book to read is *The King's Day* by Aliki, A Day in the Life of King Louis the Fourteenth.
I WONDER WHY.....I

____
____
____
____
____
____
____
____

WHEN I COULD
________________________________ INSTEAD!

The Rough-Face Girl by Rafe Martin. Illustrated by David Shannon. Putnam's, 1992.

1. Before sharing the booktalk, work with a partner or small group to put these words in no more than five groups. Be able to state the reasons for your groupings, that is, how the words in a single group are related.

powerful	wigwam	reeds	bow
scarred	rich	sled runners	arrows
Milky Way	burnt	cracked moccasins	ugly
bark	brother	broken shells	

Booktalk

In a painted wigwam by the shores of Lake Ontario lived a rich, powerful Invisible Being. All of the young women wanted to marry him because he was supposedly very handsome. But to marry the Invisible Being the women had to prove to his sister that they had seen him by describing his bow and arrows which formed a rainbow and his sled runners which made up the Milky Way. None had been able to get past the sister's stern, all-knowing gaze.

Then came the ugly Rough-Face Girl, scarred and burnt with charred hair from working by the fire. Could she succeed where her beautiful, cruel sisters had failed? They had costly clothes while she could adorn herself only in broken shells, reeds, tree bark and cracked moccasins.

From the Algonquin Indian folklore comes one of the most haunting, powerful versions of the Cinderella tale ever told.

The Booktalk as a Readers Theatre Script

Reading Parts: Narrator One, Narrator Two, Two Young Women, Rough-Face Girl, Invisible Being

Invisible Being: In a painted wigwam by the shores of Lake Ontario

Narrator Two: lived a rich, powerful Invisible Being. All of the young women

Young Women: wanted to marry him because he was supposedly very handsome.

Narrator Two: But to marry the Invisible Being the women

Young Women: had to prove to his sister

Narrator Two:	that they had seen him by describing his bow and arrows which formed a rainbow
Narrator One:	and his sled runners which made up the Milky Way. None
Young Women:	had been able to get past the sister's stern, all-knowing gaze.
Narrator One:	Then came the ugly Rough-Face Girl,
Girl:	scarred and burnt with charred hair from working by the fire.
Narrator One:	Could she succeed where her beautiful, cruel sisters had failed? They had costly clothes while she could adorn herself
Girl:	only in broken shells, reeds, tree bark and cracked moccasins.
Narrator Two:	From the Algonquin Indian folklore comes
ALL:	one of the most haunting, powerful versions of the Cinderella tale ever told.

2. After hearing the booktalk, sort the words previously grouped into two groups: (a) words that relate to the Invisible Being and (b) words that relate to the Rough-Face Girl. Use the Venn diagram below and place words in the intersecting circles that apply to both the Invisible Being and the Rough-Face Girl.

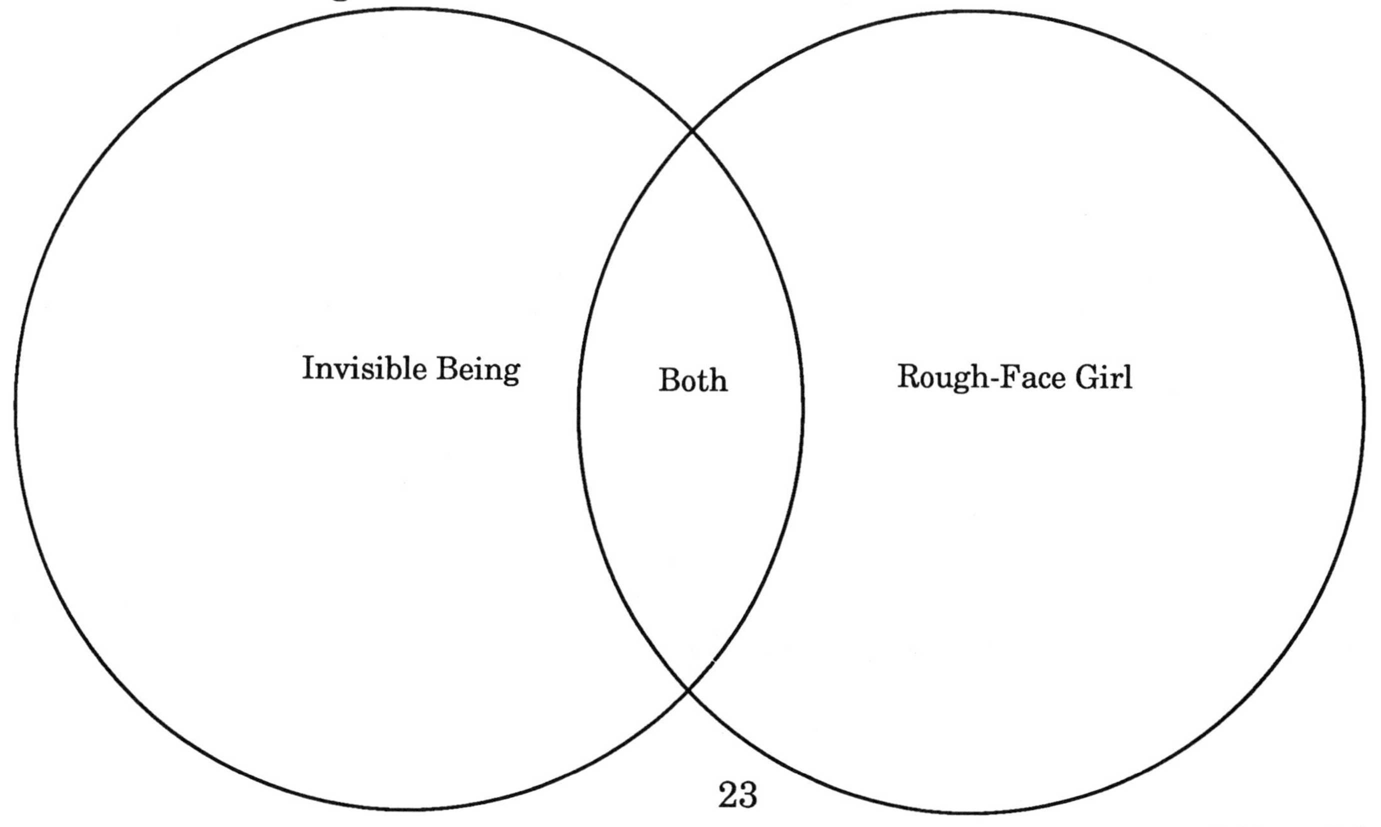

3. **A Writing Challenge**

Fill in the blank spaces of this last paragraph of the Rough-Face Girl with words you feel are appropriate. Then read the last paragraph to compare your choices with the author's.

So the Rough-Face Girl (1) __________ in the waters of the (2) __________. Suddenly all the (3) __________ vanished from her (4) ____________. Her (5) _______________ grew (6) _____________ again and her beautiful black (7) __________ grew in long and glossy as a (8) _____________ wing. Now anyone could see that she was, indeed, (9) ________________. But the (10) __________ __________ and his (11) ____________ had seen that from the start.

Author's Word Choices: 1. bathed 2. lake 3. scars 4. body 5. skin 6. smooth 7. hair 8. raven's 9. beautiful 10. Invisible Being 11. sister.

4. Cause and Effect

For each statement below list one cause and one effect.

CAUSE		EFFECT
	A. Many women wanted to marry the Invisible Being.	
	B. The two older daughters were cruel and hard-hearted.	
	C. The girl's face was marked by scars and her hair was charred.	
	D. The cruel sisters lied to the sister of the Invisible Being.	
	E. The Rough-Face Girl made a dress and leggings from birch bark.	

5. Word Game!

Use two four member teams. One person on each team must act out the word list for that team. Team members must guess the word. The team that guesses all words on its list in the shortest time is the winner.

Team A: wigwam, sled, moccasins, brother, bow

Team B: fire, arrow, Milky Way, sister, lake

Pick A Project!
A Research Organizer

Step One: Choose and circle one action word	**Step Two: Choose and circle one topic**	**Step Three: Choose and circle one product**
Label	Literature-Related Topics	Riddle Poem
List	The character of the Rough-Face Girl and the characters of her sisters.	Chart
Describe	The theme of injustice in the story.	Story
Locate	The role of the sister of the Invisible Being.	Model
Report	The Indian village as the story setting.	Map
Show	How the Invisible Being's sister is like Cinderella's fairy godmother.	Mobile
Group	Non Fiction Topics	Diorama
Discover	The Algonquin Indians-village life	Bio-poem
Compose	The art of the Algonquin Indians	Report
Create	How moccasins are made.	True/false book
Demonstrate	The Algonquin as a hunter.	Drawing
Choose	Similarities and differences with other Indian tribes	List report
Tell About	Lake Ontario	Song
		Interview

Write a sentence telling what you will do to report on the topic you choose. In your sentence include an action word and a product as well as your topic.

action — topic — product

I will **describe Algonquin village life** in a **free verse riddle poem.**

About the Algonquin Indians

The shores of Lake Ontario were the home of the Algonquin Indians. They were hunters and traders and entirely self-sufficient. The tribe was close knit and women never left the camp. They worked together for the good of all and revered nature. They killed only wildlife that was needed for food or clothing and carefully burned off dry grasses and dead wood to make way for new spring grass each year to provide a good hunting ground for the tribe.

A Free Verse Model

Here is a description of the Indian camp from *The Rough-Face Girl*. Choose another Indian tribe. Follow the model and write about it.

LET'S GO TO LONG AGO PLACES
AND SEE THE EARTH'S MANY
FACES:

Huge wigwam
Painted with sun, moon and stars
Set against tall fir trees
Beside a shimmering lake
Smaller wigwams
With cooking fires

BUT THAT'S NOT ALL

Women parading
In buckskin dresses and beaded moccasins
Watched by hidden eyes
Fingers pointing
At the Rough-Face Girl
Who just kept walking.

WHERE AM I?
An Algonquin Indian Village

LET'S GO TO LONG AGO PLACES
AND SEE THE EARTH'S MANY
FACES:

1. ______________________
2. ______________________
3. ______________________
4. ______________________
5. ______________________
6. ______________________

BUT THAT'S NOT ALL

1. ______________________
2. ______________________
3. ______________________
4. ______________________
5. ______________________
6. ______________________

WHERE AM I?
(Answer) ______________

Tattercoats: An Old English Tale retold by Flora Annie Steele. Illustrated by Diane Goode. Bradbury Press, 1976.

Booktalk

The girl called Tattercoats ran unhappily from the kitchen to find her friend, the gooseherd. He was her only companion, an odd, magical chap who, when Tattercoats was hungry and cold or tired, would play to her so gaily on his little pipe, that she would forget all her troubles and fall to dancing with his flock of noisy geese for partners.

Perhaps he would play to her now. More than anything, she wished she could see the grand doings at the King's ball, where this very night the Prince was to select his bride. But she had merely tatters from the ragbag to wear, and had been left home by her bitter old grandfather who had already set off for the festivities.

The gooseherd knew just what to do. "Take fortune when it comes, little one," he said, reaching for her hand and starting her along the way to the King's ballroom. There, before the King and the Prince and all the lords and ladies, the gooseherd played once again a magical tune-a few notes only, but enough, so that everyone saw Tattercoats for herself.

The Booktalk as a Readers Theatre Script

Speaking Parts: Narrator One, Tattercoats, Gooseherd, Narrator Two

Narrator One:	The girl called Tattercoats
Tattercoats:	ran unhappily from the kitchen to find her friend, the gooseherd.
Narrator Two:	He was
Gooseherd:	her only companion,
Narrator Two:	an odd, magical chap who, when Tattercoats was
Tattercoats:	hungry and cold or tired,
Gooseherd:	would play to her so gaily
Narrator Two:	on his little pipe, that she would forget all her troubles and
Tattercoats:	fall to dancing with his flock of noisy geese for partners.
Narrator One;	Perhaps he would play to her now. More than anything, she wished she
Tattercoats:	could see the grand doings at the King's ball, where this very night the Prince was to select his bride.

Narrator One:	But she had merely
Tattercoats:	tatters from the ragbag to wear,
Narrator One:	and had been left out by her bitter old grandfather who had already set off for the festivities.
Narrator Two:	The gooseherd
Gooseherd:	knew just what to do. "Take fortune when it comes, little one,"
Narrator Two:	he said, reaching for her hand and
Gooseherd:	starting her along the way to the King's ballroom.
Narrator Two:	There, before the King and the Prince and all the lords and ladies, the gooseherd
Gooseherd:	played once again a magical tune-a few notes only,
Narrator One:	but enough, so that everyone saw Tattercoats for herself.

2. Create a mobile similar to the one below to show the basic elements of the story. On the front of each card draw a picture of the character, setting or portion of the plot. On the back of each card write a brief description. Construct your mobile from a coat hanger attaching items from top to bottom.

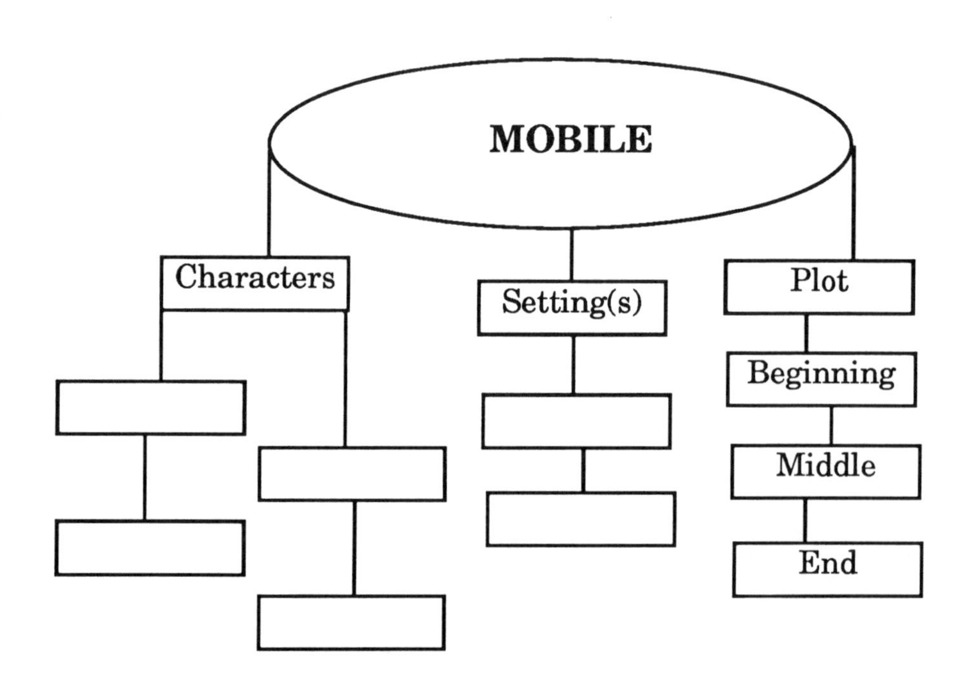

3. Comparing Characters

Use the patterns below to compare characters in Tattercoats.

A. If I had the ________________ of the grandfather
I would ____
And I would _____________________________________
But I wouldn't ___________________________________
Because the old nurse did that.

B. If I had the ________________ of the old nurse
I would ____
And I would _____________________________________
But I wouldn't ___________________________________
Because the gooseherd did that.

C. If I had the ____________________ of the gooseherd
I would ____
And I would ____________________________________
But I wouldn't ___________________________________
Because Tattercoats did that.

4. Summarize the plot of the story using the "Fortunately, Unfortunately" pattern. The first line is done for you.

FORTUNATELY <u>Tattercoats lived in a castle with her grandfather.</u>
UNFORTUNATELY ____

FORTUNATELY ____
UNFORTUNATELY ____

FORTUNATELY ____
UNFORTUNATELY ____

FORTUNATELY ____
UNFORTUNATELY ____

FORTUNATELY ____
UNFORTUNATELY ____

BUT FORTUNATELY ______________________________________
And they lived happily ever after!

Pick A Project!
A Research Organizer

Step One: Choose and circle one action word	**Step Two: Choose and circle one topic**	**Step Three: Choose and circle one product**
	<u>Literature-Related Topics</u>	
Label	The treatment of Tattercoats by her grandfather	Acrostic poem
List	The treatment of Tattercoats by the gooseherd	Chart
Describe	The role of music in the story	Story
Locate	Ways in which this story is like *The Rough-Face Girl*	Model
Report	Ways in which this story is like *The Egyptian Cinderella* and ways in which it is different	Map
Show		Mobile
Group	<u>Non Fiction Topics</u>	Diorama
Discover	The job of a gooseherd	Bio-poem
Compose	Buckingham Palace	Report
Create	A famous castle in England	Fact or Fiction book
Demonstrate	English traditions	Drawing
Choose	One famous King of England	List report
Tell About	A day in the life of a King	Song
	A day in the life of a real princess	Interview

Write a sentence telling what you will do to report on the topic you choose. In your sentence include an action word and a product as well as your topic.

action — topic — product

I will **report** on **English traditions** in a **Fact or Fiction book**.

Tattercoats: An Old English Tale continued.

English Traditions

The English people love tradition. Many traditions are hundreds of years old. In Olney on the day before Lent begins the housewives bake pancakes. At noon they meet in the village square and race to the church door, each holding a griddle with a hot pancake in it. They must flip the pancake at least three times during the race. The winner receives a "kiss of peace" from the village caretaker.

In Lichfield the sheriff must ride the boundaries of the city every September 8th. He is carrying out the order of Queen Mary the First who in 1553 ordered the sheriff to check each boundary marker once each year.

Boxing Day, the first day after Christmas is still a holiday. It was named for an old tradition that called for young workers to carry boxes around to their masters' customers asking for tips.

Research other English traditions. Create a Fact or Fiction book about them.

Vasilisa the Beautiful translated from the Russian by Thomas P. Whitney. Illustrated by Nonny Hogrogian. Macmillan, 1970.
Vasilisa the Beautiful by Elizabeth Winthrop. Illustrated by Alexander Koshkin. HarperCollins, 1991.

Booktalk

Vasilisa was despised and mistreated by her stepmother and stepsisters. She was given all of the work to do in the home, only scraps to eat and a cold storeroom in which to live. Her only comfort came from the small doll given to her by her mother just before her mother's death.

One dark night Vasilisa is made to go into the forest to get a light from the evil Baba Yaga who lives alone in a hut that stands on chicken legs. This evil witch eats any person who is foolish enough to bother her.

Vasilisa is taken into Baba Yaga's hut and given many difficult tasks to do. She must clean house, make dinner, wash linens, clean bushels of wheat of the weed seeds, and remove the dirt from each poppy seed. Again the doll brings comfort and does each task for Vasilisa.

When Baba Yaga discovers that the child has been blessed, she sends her on her way with a light inside a skull. The rays of light destroy the stepmother and stepsisters and Vasilisa goes to the city to live. To pay for her keep she spins yarn and makes cloth...the finest ever seen! How the cloth brings Vasilisa and the King together makes an exciting story. Read the Russian Cinderella, *Vasilisa the Beautiful*.

The Booktalk as a Readers Theatre Script

Reading Parts: Vasilisa, Stepmother, Doll, Baba Yaga, Narrator One, Narrator Two
Narrator Two: Vasilisa was
Stepmother: despised and mistreated
Narrator Two: by her stepmother and stepsisters.
Narrator One: She was
Vasilisa: given all of the work to do in the home, only scraps to eat and a cold storeroom in which to live.
Narrator One: Her only comfort came from the small doll
Doll: given to her by her mother just before her mother's death.
Narrator One: One dark night Vasilisa is made to go into the forest
Vasilisa: to get a light from the evil Baba Yaga who
Baba Yaga: lives alone in a hut that stands on chicken legs.

Vasilisa the Beautiful continued.

Narrator Two:	This evil witch
Baba Yaga:	eats any person who is foolish enough
Narrator Two:	to bother her.
Narrator One:	Vasilisa is taken
Vasilisa:	into Baba Yaga's hut and given many difficult tasks to do.
Narrator One:	She must
Baba Yaga:	clean house, make dinner, wash linens, clean bushels of wheat of the weed seeds, and remove the dirt from each poppy seed.
Narrator One:	Again the doll
Doll:	brings comfort and does each task for Vasilisa.
Narrator Two:	When Baba Yaga discovers
Baba Yaga:	that the child has been blessed,
Narrator Two:	she sends her on her way with a light
Baba Yaga:	inside a skull.
Narrator Two:	The rays of light destroy the stepmother and stepsisters and
Narrator One:	Vasilisa goes to the city to live. To pay for her keep she
Vasilisa:	spins yarn and makes cloth...the finest ever seen!
Narrator One:	How the cloth brings Vasilisa and the King together makes an exciting story.
ALL:	Read the Russian Cinderella, *Vasilisa the Beautiful.*

Write About A Character! Or A Setting!

Use the Bio-poem model that follows to write about Vasilisa or Baba Yaga. Or use the Five Senses Poem model to write about Baba Yaga's hut.

Bio Poem

Line	
1	First name
2	Four traits
3	Related to
4	Cares deeply about
5	Who feels
6	Who needs
7	Who gives
8	Who fears
9	Who would like to see
10	Resident of

Five Senses Poem

Line		
1	Color	Baba Yaga's hut is the color of ____________________
2	Sound	It sounds like ________________
3	Taste	It tastes like __________________
4	Smell	It smells like _________________
5	Sight	It looks like __________________
6	Feeling	It makes me feel like ___________

A Classroom Game: Guess Who You Are!

1. Make signs or label pictures for the following:

Vasilisa	Stepmother	Stepsister who weaves lace
Doll	King	Stepsister who knits stockings
Red Horseman	The White Horseman	The Black Horseman
Baba Yaga	Kind Foster Mother	

2. The sign or labeled picture is pinned to the back of a student.

3. Students walk around and talk to each other as if each was the famous person indicated by the sign.
   Example: The Black horseman might hear the following:
   "I'm glad to see you are keeping out of the sun."
   "It would be hard to travel with only two legs, wouldn't it?"
   "You don't seem to care much for bright colors, do you?"

4. When a student guesses correctly who he or she is, the sign is taken off and held in the hand.

5. Students wearing signs can also ask others questions about the character they are supposed to be but their questions cannot use the name of any character.
   Example: "Do I usually ride instead of walking?" (yes)
   "Is my favorite color red?" (no)
   All questions must be answered by only yes or no.

   <u>Variation</u>
   1. A student chooses to be one character from the story and lists five clues about the character.
   2. A volunteer from the class names a number between one and five.
   3. The student who is giving the report reads the clue for that number.
   4. Players who are given clues can guess or pass.
   5. The game continues until the character is guessed or all clues are read.

Pick A Project!
A Research Organizer

Step One: Choose and circle one action word	**Step Two: Choose and circle one topic**	**Step Three: Choose and circle one product**
Label List Describe Locate Report Show Group Discover Compose Create Demonstrate Choose Tell About	<u>Literature-Related Topics</u> The changing moods of the story The theme of unselfishness as shown in the story How Baba Yaga and the stepmother are alike and different How the doll in the story is similar to the fairy godmother in Cinderella <u>Non Fiction Topics</u> A typical day for a child living in Moscow Things that the Russian people do for enjoyment Famous buildings in Moscow Wintertime in Russia Living in Russia	Acrostic poem Chart Story Model Game Mobile Diorama Bio-poem Report True/false book Drawing List report Song Tic Tac Toe game Interview

Write a sentence telling what you will do to report on the topic you choose. In your sentence include an action word and a product as well as your topic.

action / topic / product

I will **report** on **living in Russia** using a **tic tac toe game**.

About Russia by Jonet Jaggers

Russia is one part of the former Soviet Union which has undergone many changes in the past decade. Moscow, the capital city, has many interesting buildings. The most famous buildings are the government headquarters known as The Kremlin. The government of the former Soviet Union was first ruled by kings and czars. In the early 1900's the czar of Russia was forced to give up his throne and a dictator took over. A dictator is one person who rules a country. In the 1980's Gorbachev headed the government and led the way to many changes giving more freedom to the people.

People in Russia enjoy doing many of the same things you enjoy. They enjoy taking rides in a troika, a sleigh drawn by three horses, and dancing the Pereplyas, which is a Russian folkdance where five people try to outdo each other in skill and in making new steps. Children in Russia also enjoy playing with seven stacking dolls called Matryoshka.

How well did you read (or listen)? Play a game of tic-tac-toe with a friend. Complete any three squares down, across, or diagonally.

Moscow

Siberia

Pereplyas

dictator

czar

Gorbachev

Kremlin

Troika

Matryoshka

A famous group of buildings in the former Soviet Union	A folk dance	Single ruler of a country
Sleigh drawn by three horses	City in Russia	Seven stacking dolls
He began changes in Russia to give people more freedom	Early Russian Ruler	Land east of the Ural Mountains

Yeh-Shen: A Cinderella Story From China retold by Ai-Ling Louie. Illustrated by Ed Young. Philomel Books, 1982.

1. Pre Reading Sentence Starters
   Choose one of the sentence starters below and write about it for five minutes. Be prepared to share what you have written with a small group.
   a. If a very poor person could have one wish it would be ____________ because.....
   b. An older sister can sometimes.....
   c. A fish makes a good pet when.....
   d. Taking a precious object guarded by soldiers is not a crime when.....
2. What will you predict?
   Some part of this Chinese Cinderella story will be different from the Cinderella tale with which you are familiar. Before hearing the booktalk, predict the correct answer to each question that follows:
   A. The Chinese Cinderella has: (a) one stepsister (b) two stepsisters (c) three stepsisters
   B. She lives in (a) a large house (b) a cave (c) a small house
   C. She is helped by (a) a fairy godmother (b) an old man (c) an old woman
   D. Her wishes are granted by (a) magic fish bones (b) a magic wand (c) a willow tree
   E. She wanted to go to (a) a ball (b) a town (c) a festival
   F. In the end she marries (a) a king (b) a rich man (c) a prince

Booktalk

Long ago in southern China there was a beautiful girl named Yeh-Shen. Her own mother died when she was a baby, and her father, too, died soon after, leaving Yeh-Shen in the care of a stepmother, who treated her very badly. Now poor Yeh-Shen was dressed in rags, and made to do all the hard work in the cave where they lived. Her only friend was a fish that her stepmother killed and ate. In her sorrow, Yeh-Shen is visited by an old man who tells her that the fish bones are magic and will grant her any wish. So at festival time while Stepmother and Stepsister when off dancing, Yeh-Shen made her wish. In an instant she had beautiful clothes and golden slippers that the spirit of the bones warned her not to lose. But alas, at the festival in a rush not to be seen by Stepmother, Yeh-Shen loses a slipper. When she returns home the bones are silent. Little does she know that the King has vowed never to rest until the girl who lost the slipper is found. To discover how this happy ending comes about, read *Yeh-Shen: A Cinderella Story From China.*

The Booktalk as a Readers Theatre Script

Reading Parts:	Narrator One, Narrator Two, Yeh-Shen, Stepmother, Old Man, King
Narrator One:	Long ago in southern China there was a beautiful girl named Yeh-Shen. Her own mother died when she
Yeh-Shen:	was a baby,
Narrator Two:	and her father, too, died soon after,
Narrator One:	leaving Yeh-Shen
Yeh-Shen:	in the care of a stepmother, who
Stepmother:	treated her very badly.
Narrator One:	Now poor Yeh-Shen
Yeh-Shen:	was dressed in rags, and made to do all the hard work
Narrator Two:	in the cave where they lived. Her only friend was a fish that her stepmother
Stepmother:	killed and ate.
Narrator One:	In her sorrow, Yeh-Shen is visited by an old man who
Old Man:	tells her that the fish bones are magic and will grant her any wish.
Narrator Two:	So at festival time while Stepmother and Stepsister went off dancing,
Narrator One:	Yeh-Shen made her wish. In an instant she had
Yeh-Shen:	beautiful clothes and golden slippers that
Narrator Two:	the spirit of the bones warned her not to lose. But alas, at the festival
Yeh-Shen:	in a rush not to be seen by Stepmother,
Narrator One:	Yeh-Shen
Yeh-Shen:	loses a slipper.
Narrator One:	When she returns home the bones are silent. Little does she know that the King
King:	has vowed never to rest until the girl who lost the slipper is found.
NARRATORS:	To discover how this happy ending comes about,
ALL:	read *Yeh-Shen: A Cinderella Story From China.*

3. Clue Cards: Pass out cards with the following words (one word per card) TIME, LOCATION, OCCUPATION, FEELINGS, PROBLEM. Who can find a sentence in the booktalk or in the story that gives a clue as to when the story took place (year? time of year? time of day?) what people did for a living, someone's feelings, the problem to be overcome, where the story took place?

Answers to the Pre Reading Quiz: What Will You Predict? A. a B. b C. b D. a E. c F. a

Character Report Cards

4. Complete the following report cards for Yeh-Shen and her stepmother. Grade each item A, B, C, D, or F. Tell why you gave each grade.

Report Card for Yeh-Shen	Report Card for Stepmother
Receives a grade of ________ in KINDNESS because ________________	Receives a grade of ________ in KINDNESS because ________________
Receives a grade of ________ in COURAGE because ________________	Receives a grade of ________ in COURAGE because ________________
Receives a grade of ________ in WORKS HARD because ________________	Receives a grade of ________ in WORKS HARD because ________________
Receives a grade of ________ in CARING FOR WILD CREATURES because ________________	Receives a grade of ________ in CARING FOR WILD CREATURES because ________________
Receives a grade of ________ in CAVE CLEANING because ________________	Receives a grade of ________ in CAVE CLEANING because ________________

5. What Would A Character Do? Work in small groups to answer each question.
   A. What would Yeh-Shen do if she knocked over a large display in a super market?
   B. What would Stepmother do in the same situation?

   A. What would Stepmother do if a robber tried to grab her bag at the festival?
   B. What would Yeh-Shen do in the same situation?

   A. What would Yeh-Shen do if she found a hungry puppy on the road?
   B. What would Stepmother do in the same situation?

   A. What would Yeh-Shen do if she saw a large table of food at the festival?
   B. What would Stepmother do in the same situation?

   A. What would Stepmother do if granted one wish?
   B. What would Yeh-Shen do in the same situation?

Pick A Project!
A Research Organizer

Step One: Choose and circle one action word	Step Two: Choose and circle one topic	Step Three: Choose and circle one product
Label List Describe Locate Report Show Group Discover Compose Create Demonstrate Choose Tell About Summarize	<u>Literature-Related Topics</u> The role of the old man Ways in which the stepmother was unkind Yeh-Shen's kindness to animals The setting of the story Differences in this story and in Cinderella (likenesses) The changing moods of the story <u>Non Fiction Topics</u> Crops raised in China Animals found in China The Water Buffalo The Giant Panda Chinese Festivals The Chinese New Year The Great Wall of China Important Chinese inventions Printing press Gun powder Paper	Acrostic poem Chart Story Model Mobile Diorama Bio-poem Report Process Report Drawing List report Song Interview

Write a sentence telling what you will do to report on the topic you choose. In your sentence include an action word and a product as well as your topic.

action — topic — product

I will **summarize information about the water buffalo** in a **list report**.

About China

China is the largest country in eastern Asia. More than one fifth of all the people in the world live in China. Beijing, the capital of China, has a population of 9.3 million people. The Chinese grow many crops including cotton, rice, tea and wheat. They produce many items including cotton cloth, silk and porcelain. One of nature's gifts to the Chinese people is the bamboo plant, which grows wild in China. The Chinese eat bamboo sprouts and use bamboo reeds to make furniture, to build houses and boats, to weave sandals and hats and to make pulp which is rolled into writing paper. Water buffalo are common in China and are used to plow rice paddies.

Data Bank - Water Buffalo

EATS	LIVES	HAS
grass	in China	horns
weeds	in India	tough, thick hide
hay	in the Philippines	thin hair

WHAT IT DOES	LOOKS LIKE
wallows in mud and water	very large cow
fights fiercely when wild	circular horns on males
plows rice fields	five to six feet tall
gives nourishing milk	

The information in the data bank above is used in the list report that follows. Create a data bank about another Chinese animal, the giant panda. Write a list report about the panda using the information in your data bank.

Facts about water buffalo

Eats grass
And weeds
Chews hay
In China
Likes mud
And water
These are just a few
Fights fiercely
Gives milk
Plows fields
Has horns
Tough hide
Thin hair
Six feet tall, too!
From near and far
Here they are
Facts about water buffalo

Facts about pandas

____
____
____
____
____
These are just a few
____
____
____
____
____
________________ too!
From near and far
Here they are
Facts about pandas.

Analyzing Character: Eight Cinderellas (Plus One!)

What Would the Character Do?
Make name cards for these characters: Rhodopes, Pear Blossom, Nyasha, Furball, Manyara, Rough Face Girl, Baba Yaga, Tattercoats, Vasilisa, Yeh Shen, Ashpet.
Cut apart the name cards below and place face down. The student chooses one of each and tells what the character would do in the situation.

How Would a Character Feel?
Make name cards for the main character in a story or stories students have read. Cut apart the feeling cards below and place face down. The student chooses a character card and a feeling card and completes this sentence:
Character felt feeling when ____________
________________ ____________________
(relate to a specific part of the story and justify your answer)

A. Your character is alone at night on a dark, deserted street and hears footsteps approaching.	E. Your character has done a difficult job for agreed-upon pay and the employer refuses to pay.
B. Your character is at the supermarket and knocks over a barrel of apples, spilling them all over the floor.	F. Your character is alone in a strange land where no one speaks the character's language and wants directions for getting home.
C. Your character answers the door to find a homeless person asking for food.	G. Your character is on horseback out west and faces a herd of stampeding cattle.
D. Your character is given the choice of attending a symphony concert or a rock festival.	H. Your character was left home alone by mistake. The family won't return for three days.

1 **brave**	9 **cautious**
2 **cruel**	10 **impatient**
3 **wicked**	11 **pitiful**
4 **unhappy**	12 **confused**
5 **foolish**	13 **scared**
6 **upset**	14 **helpless**
7 **happy**	15 **caring**
8 **optimistic**	16 **thoughtful**

The Cinderella Variants used in this activity book are:

The Egyptian Cinderella by Shirley Climo. Illustrated by Ruth Heller. HarperCollins, 1989.

The Korean Cinderella by Shirley Climo. Illustrated by Ruth Heller. HarperCollins, 1993.

Mufaro's Beautiful Daughters written and illustrated by John Steptoe. Scholastic, 1987.

Princess Furball by Charlotte Huck. Illustrated by Anita Lobel. Greenwillow Books, 1989.

The Rough-Face Girl by Rafe Martin. Illustrated by David Shannon. Putnam's, 1992.

Tattercoats: An Old English Tale retold by Flora Annie Stelle. Illustrated by Diane Goode. Bradbury Press, 1976.

Vasilisa the Beautiful translated from the Russian by Thomas P. Whitney. Illustrated by Nonny Hogrogian. Macmillan, 1970.

Yeh-Shen: A Cinderella Story From China retold by Ai-Ling Louie. Illustrated by Ed Young. Philomel Books, 1982.

Cinderella Variants

Cinderella References

Cinderella by Judy Sierra. Orys Press, 1992.
24 Cinderella stories from different cultures

Cinderella: 345 Variants of Cinderella, Catskin, and Cap o'Rushes by Marian Roalfe Cox. Kraus Reprint, 1967.

The Multicultural Cinderella by J.D. Rusing. Rusting Educational Services, 1994.

Cinderella's Stepsister
Cinderella, the Untold Story by Russell Shorto, Carol Publishing Group, 1990.

Cinderella Worldwide

Africa
Chinye: a West African Folk Tale retold by Obi Onyefulu. 1994.
Zulu
Nomi and the Magic Fish: a Story from Africa by Phumla, Doubleday, 1972.

Algonquin Indians
Little Firefly: an Algonquin Legend adapted by Terri Cohlene, Rourke Corporation, 1990.

Appalachian Mountains, USA
Ashpet: an Appalachian Tale retold by Joanne Compton. Holiday House, 1994.

China
Wishbones: A Folktale from China retold by Barbara Ker Wilson, Bradbury, 1993.

France
Cinderella by Charles Perrault. Scribners, 1954.

Germany
Ashputtle: A Cinderella Tale from Germany translated from the Grimm Tales by Ralph Manheim, Doubleday, 1977.

India
The Enchanted Anklet: A Cinderella Story from India translated and adapted by Lila Mehta, Lilmur, 1985.

Ireland
Billy Beg and his Bull: an Irish Tale retold by Ellin Greene. Holiday House, 1994.
The Starlight Cloak by Jenny Mimmo. Dial, 1993.

Italy
Favorite Fairy Tales Told In Italy (Cenerentola) by Virginia Haviland. Little Brown, 1965.

Japan
Lily and the Wooden Bowl by Alan Schroeder, Doubleday, 1994.
Norway
Boots and the Glass Mountain by Claire Martin. Dial Books. 1992.

Korea
Korean Cinderella edited by Edward B. Adams, Seoul International Tourist Pub. Co., 1983.

Phillipines
Abadeha, the Phillippine Cinderella by Myrna J. de la Paz. Pazific Queen, 1991.

Rap
Cinder-Elly by Frances Minters. Viking, 1994.

Russian
Baba Yaga and Vasilisa the Brave told by Marianna Mayer. Morrow Junior Books, 1994.

Southern USA
Moss Gown by William Hooks. Clarion Books, 1987.

Thailand
Kao and the Golden Fish: a Folktale from Thailand retold by Cheryl Hamada, Children's Press, 1993.

Vietnam
In the Land of Small Dragon: A Vietnamese Folktale told to Ann Nolan Clark, Viking Press, 1979.
Tam Cam: The Vietnamese Cinderella Story by The Goi.
The Brocaded Slipper by ynette Dyer Vuong. Addison Wesley, 1982.

In addition, find more variants from the Internet:

Mayan Folktales: http://www.folkart.com

Other references:

http://www-dept.usm.edu/~engdept/cindrella/cinderella.html
http://www.acs.ucalgary.ca/~dkbrown/cinderella.html